Contents **Contents** Contents

Special Features

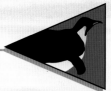

Features

I Wish I Had Long Wings

Written by Janette Johnstone • Illustrated by Kerry Gemmill

Perdita Penguin wished that she had long wings like her friend, Peter. Peter was a giant petrel.

"I wish I had long wings like you. I'm a bird that just can't fly!" Perdita said.

"Don't be silly," said Peter. "Penguins aren't supposed to fly! But I'll take you for a ride on my back if you like."

"Oh yes, that would be great fun!" said Perdita.

Peter bent down and Perdita climbed onto his back.

"You're very heavy for a little penguin," said Peter. "Hold on, here we go!"

With a few flaps of his wings, Peter flew up into the air. Perdita sat very still. She looked around and was amazed at how the Earth looked from up in the air.

"I can see for miles!" she shouted, as Peter wheeled high above the snow.

"I know," said Peter. "It is a lot of fun flying." At last, Peter flew down again.

"I wish I had long wings," said Perdita again. "But I can't even walk very fast."

"That may be so," said Peter, "but you can do things that I am not able to do."

"Like what?" said Perdita.

"You can skim along the snow and ice on your stomach," said Peter. "I can't do that!"

"Yes, I can," said Perdita, sadly. "But that's not as much fun as flying. I would much rather fly than skim along the ice on my stomach."

"We can go for a walk together," said Peter. "I don't walk much faster than you do."

So Perdita and Peter went for a walk across the ice. Perdita waddled along as fast as she could go.

They had been walking for about ten minutes when Perdita noticed something on the ice just ahead of them. She couldn't quite make out what it was. But, as they got closer, she realized that it was trouble!

"Be careful, Peter," said Perdita. "There's a slippery patch of oil on the ice, and the ice looks very thin here."

But Perdita's warning came too late. Peter slipped on the oil. Crrrr-ack! Just as she gave her warning, the ice broke and Peter fell into the cold water! He was trapped. His wings had oil on them so he couldn't fly.

"Hold on, Peter!" shouted Perdita. "I'll go and get some help!"

Perdita jumped into the water and swam away under the ice. She knew she would need help to keep Peter afloat. He was too big for her to do it by herself.

In no time at all, she swam back with Elizabeth Emperor, another penguin.

"If you relax and don't struggle it'll be easier for us to help you," said Elizabeth.

So Peter relaxed while Perdita and Elizabeth went to work.

"Don't worry, Peter," said Perdita. "We'll get you out."

Perdita and Elizabeth swam under Peter's long wings and pushed him up out of the water. They pushed and pushed. At last, they all sat on the edge of the ice, puffing.

"Thank you both for making such a speedy rescue," said Peter. Then he started to clean the oil off his feathers.

It would take a long time to get all of the oil out of his feathers, but Peter was so glad to get out of the cold water he didn't mind doing all the cleaning.

Although the water had been cold, Perdita felt warm and happy.

"You know, I'm glad I have short wings!" she said. "They're like flippers. They help me swim faster. And I think I would look silly with long wings."

"I'm glad you've got short wings, too," said Peter. "If you didn't have short wings you might not have been able to save me!"

"Of course you would look silly with long wings," said Elizabeth Emperor. "Who ever heard of a penguin that could fly?"

"I guess we should all be happy with what we've got!" said Perdita.

Safari POWER

Word Meanings

burrow
- a – donkey
- b – hole in the ground
- c – cheese

excellent
- a – mean
- b – poor
- c – very good

glee
- a – grumpiness
- b – delight
- c – speed

proud
- a – plain
- b – humble
- c – vain

speedy
- a – skinny
- b – slow
- c – fast

surfer
- a – someone who rides waves
- b – someone who runs fast
- c – someone who swims well

tumble
- a – make a lot of noise
- b – fall suddenly
- c – talk quietly

waddle
- a – move like a duck
- b – move like a horse
- c – move like a cat

a, b, or c?

Answers on page 21

10

Who Am I?

Written by Sally Cole

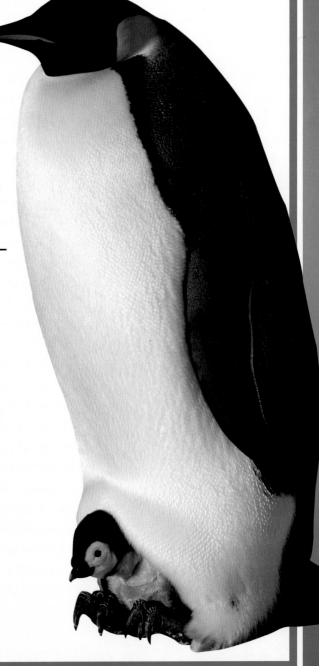

You should call me Highness,
As I'm really royalty.
I'm as important as a king –
An excellent bird, that's me!

I'm tall and proud, I dress in black,
With a white shirt front, you see.
A touch of gold worn on my head –
An excellent bird, that's me!

I hold my babies on my feet
To keep them warm by me.
I dive down deep, I swim so fast –
An excellent bird, that's me!

Can you guess what bird I am?
How royal I must be?
Yes, I'm an emperor penguin –
An excellent bird, that's me!

Amazing Emperor Penguins

Written by Bob Eschenbach

Do You Know This Bird?

Do you know a bird that can dive down 900 feet (274 m) into the ocean? Do you know a bird that travels a long way to breed? Do you know a bird that does not eat for months at a time?

This bird is the emperor penguin that lives in Antarctica.

Size

Emperor penguins can grow up to 4 feet (1.2 m) tall. They also can weigh up to 100 pounds (45 kg).

Emperor penguins are almost 4 feet (1.2 m) tall.

Swimming and Diving

Emperor penguins spend most of their time in the ocean. They are good swimmers and use their flippers like paddles.

They can swim up to 15 miles per hour (24 kph).

Emperor penguins can dive as deep as 900 feet (274 m) when they are hunting for food. They can hold their breath for as long as 20 minutes.

Food

Emperor penguins eat krill, squid, and small fish. They catch their prey by swimming after them.

Emperor penguins jumping out of the water after they have eaten.

In summer, they eat a lot of fish to get as fat as they can for the long winter. Their fat keeps them warm in very cold temperatures. In Antarctica, the winter temperatures can get down to -68° F (-55° C).

Breeding

Emperor penguins come onto the ice to breed in early winter. They travel a long way from the ocean, across the ice.

Emperor penguins huddle together in rookeries.

When they find a safe place, the penguins stand in a big huddle to keep warm. This is where the penguins will lay their eggs. These places are called rookeries.

Female penguins lay one egg. They roll the egg onto the feet of the male penguins. The males cover the eggs with their stomach skin to keep them warm.

Female penguins then leave the males to look after the eggs. They go to feed in the ocean. They can be gone for as long as two months. The males do not eat for all that time. They live on the fat they have stored since summer. The males can lose between a third and a half of their body weight while they are looking after their eggs.

Female penguins hunt for up to two months after laying their eggs.

Female penguins come back to the rookery in spring, just in time for the chicks to hatch. The male penguins then give the chicks to the females. The males have to give the chicks to the females quickly. If they take too long the chicks will freeze to death. Now the females keep the chicks warm under their stomach skin while the male penguins go back to the ocean to feed.

The males and the females take turns feeding and keeping the chicks warm until summer.

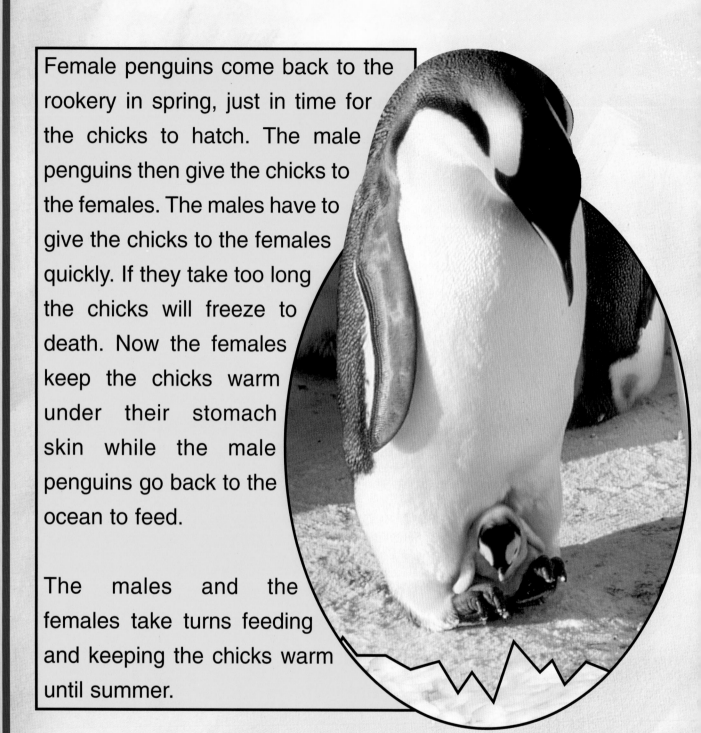

Until they become adults, the chicks have to be careful not to be caught by leopard seals or orca whales. Leopard seals and orcas will eat the young chicks if they catch them at sea. Leopard seals are too slow to catch baby penguins on land.

When emperor penguin chicks are four months old, they are ready to go fishing for themselves.

Safari CLASSIFIEDS

FOR SALE

FRESH FISH

Different kinds of fish. Caught daily. Call Emperor Fish Mart with your order today. Free delivery with phone orders!

Call
Emperor Fish Mart.

FOR SALE

PHOTOGRAPHS

of Antarctic birds for sale. Penguins, petrels, and skuas. Make great gifts. Cheap rates if you order more than one set of photographs.

Call or fax
Ice Photography.

HELP WANTED

BABYSITTER WANTED

Must be patient and good with little birds. Position would be suitable for an emperor penguin with no children.

Call Mrs. Bird.

TRAVEL

VISIT

the exciting South Island of New Zealand. See fairy penguins in the wild. Great deals available.

Call
Penguin Travel now!

Safari POWER

burrow
b – hole in the ground

excellent
c – very good

glee
b – delight

speedy
c – fast

proud
c – vain

surfer
a – someone who rides waves

tumble
b – fall suddenly

waddle
a – move like a duck

Xtra for Xperts

What are rookeries?

Rating Scale

7-8 Excellent   5-6 Very good   3-4 Good   0-2 Try again

Penguins
on Parade

A one-act play

Written by Dale Harcombe
Illustrated by Caroline Beaufort

Dad

Moana

Narrator

Person in the Crowd

Narrator

Moana and her dad are on a beach in New Zealand. They have come for a special reason. There are a lot of other people with them.

Moana

How much longer do we have to wait, Dad? It seems as if we've been here for a very long time.

Dad

It won't be too long now, Moana. We have to wait until the sun goes down.

Moana

How much longer before the sun goes down, Dad?

Dad

Soon. Very soon, Moana. You can just see the edge of the sun starting to dip into the sea.

Moana

Soon seems a long time, Dad.
But you're right, I can see
the sun. It's almost gone.

Narrator

Five minutes later the
sun has gone down at last.

Moana

How much longer now, Dad?

Dad

It won't be long now. Fairy penguins come up onto the beach when it gets dark.

Narrator

Moana waits and watches the sea. Moana sees something move out of the corner of her eye.

Moana

I can see one! Look!

Narrator

Everyone jumps up to look, but it's not what they're waiting for.

Person in the Crowd

No, it's not. It's a seagull. Don't worry. It's easy to get them mixed up with penguins when it's getting dark.

Moana

How much longer do we have to wait, Dad? I thought the penguins would be here by now.

Dad

They don't come out as soon as it gets dark, but it won't be long now. Keep watching.

Narrator

Moana keeps waiting and watching the sea.

Person in the Crowd

There they are! I can see them!

Narrator

Yes, the waiting's over! The fairy penguins swim in on waves! They're like surfers! They come out onto the sand and then stop. They look around. Then they hurry back to the water.

Moana

Don't they look cute! Oh! The penguins are running away!

Dad

Just wait, they'll come back. They're not running away. They are running back into the waves to make sure all their friends have made it back from hunting.

Narrator

One brave penguin comes out of the water again. The other penguins follow. Then they all hurry back to the water. They keep on coming in and out of the water. They seem to be having a lot of fun.

Moana

I hope they haven't gone far.
I really want to see them again.
When will they come out again, Dad?

Dad

Just wait, they'll come back soon.

Narrator

Moana can hear the penguins calling to each other.

As they reach the sand, the penguins stop.

Moana holds her breath.

Will they stay this time? Yes!

They hurry across the sand on their short legs.

Person in the Crowd

They are coming over to where we are. They look like they're in a hurry to get to their burrows.

Moana

Can we get closer to the penguins, Dad?

I could reach out and touch one.

Dad

No, you would scare them. Fairy penguins are very shy. And we should always leave animals in the wild alone.

Narrator

The fairy penguins climb the sand dunes to their burrows. One late penguin hurries up the beach. The penguin is near Moana's feet. She could touch it! But she remembers what her dad said, and she doesn't. The fairy penguin waddles up the sand dune and into its burrow.

Dad

Well, Moana, was it worth the wait?

Moana

Oh, yes!

Narrator

Moana, her dad, and the rest of the people get up and start to walk away quietly. They don't want to disturb the penguins.

Eight Little Penguins

Written by Cheryl Ryan
Illustrated by Donna Cross

In a faraway land where cold winds blow,
Eight little penguins went sledding in the snow.
They glided and slid down hills of ice!
Eight little penguins thought sledding was nice.

They romped and slid the whole day long,
And eight little penguins sang a happy song.
They hopped and jumped with joyful glee,
They were the happiest penguins you'd ever see!

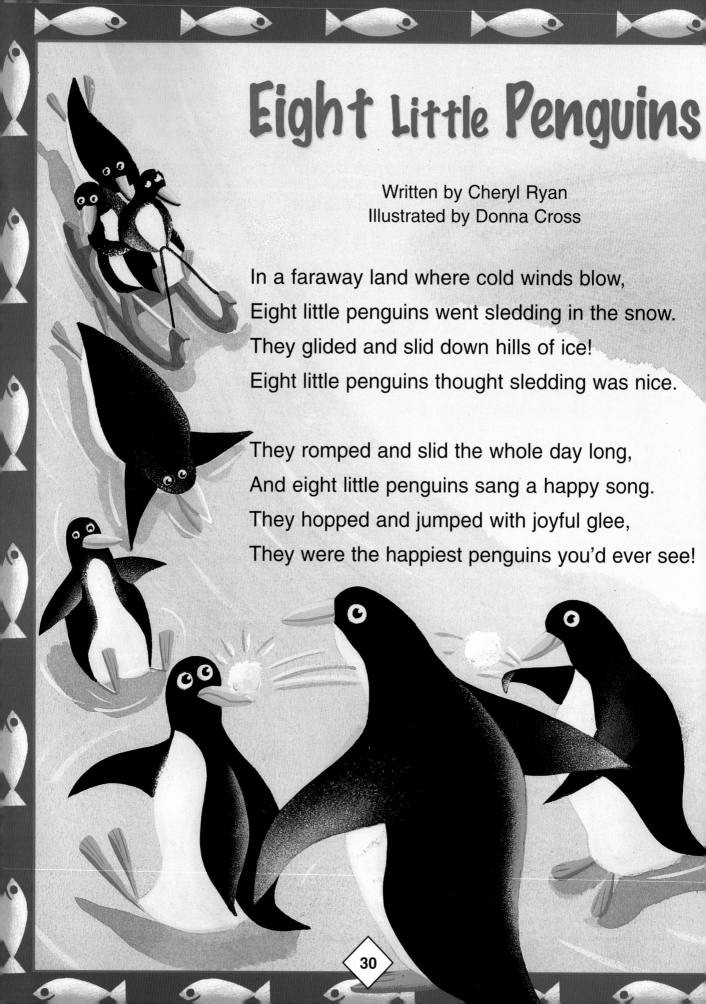

The eight little penguins held a race,

And they all had hopes of getting first place.

The eight little penguins were in teams of two.

Off they went! Down the hill they flew!

The first team flipped and slid over an icy cliff,

And when they got up, they were sore and stiff.

The second team hit the ocean, what a place to be!

And those two penguins were a sorry sight to see.

The third team of two tumbled and rolled,

And they ended up chilly and cold.

The last team flew at a furious pace,

And they were the two that won the race!

readingsafari.com

Check out these Safari magazines, too!

Have your say –

e-mail your Safari Tour Guide at
tourguide@readingsafari.com

Safari Tour Guide, 40

I have seen fairy penguins on parade, too. I have written a poem about them.

Aaron Walsh (7)

Find some fun things to do!

Go to –
http://www.readingsafari.com

Safari Superstar

Name – Moana

Birthday – November 30

Find out more about this Safari Superstar at
http://www.readingsafari.com